Book 1

Sure-fire Phonics

Ann Williams and Jim Rogerson

Illustrated by Oxford Illustrators Limited

ARNOLD-WHEATON

Arnold-Wheaton
A Division of E. J. Arnold & Son Limited
Parkside Lane, Leeds, LS11 5TD

A subsidiary of Pergamon Press Ltd.,
Headington Hill Hall, Oxford, OX3 0BW

Pergamon Press Inc.,
Maxwell House, Fairview Park, Elmsford, New York 10523

Pergamon Press Canada Ltd.,
Suite 104, 150 Consumers Road, Willowdale, Ontario
M2J 1P9

Pergamon Press (Australia) Pty Ltd.,
P.O. Box 544, Potts Point, N.S.W. 2011

Pergamon Press GmbH
Hammerweg 6, D-6242 Kronberg,
Federal Republic of Germany

First Published 1980
Reprinted 1981, 1983, 1984, 1986

Printed in Great Britain by A. Wheaton & Co. Ltd., Exeter (TS)
ISBN 0-08-024344-4

Contents

The simple sound **a** as in apple   2
The simple sound **e** as in egg   3
The simple sound **i** as in ink   4
The simple sound **o** as in orange   5
The simple sound **u** as in umbrella   6
Revision of the sounds **a**, **e**, **i**, **o** and **u**   7
The simple sound **m** as in man   8
The simple sound **t** as in tap   9
Finding **m** words. Finding **t** words   10
Who is this? Look at the picture. Write the word   11
The simple sound **s** as in sack   12
Finding **s** words. Who sits?   13
The simple sound **n** as in net   14
Look at the picture. Write the word   15
The simple sound **p** as in pan   16
Look at the picture. Write the word   17
The simple sound **c** as in cat   18
Finding **c** words. Look at the picture. Write the word   19
The simple sound **k** as in king   20
Look at the picture. Write the word   21
The simple sound **f** as in fan   22
Finding **f** words. Choose the right **f** word   23
The sight word **I**. Look at the picture. Write the word   24
The sight word **the**. Find the right words in the bag   25
The simple sound **l** as in log   26
Complete the sentences: **l** words   27
The simple sound **b** as in bed   28
Complete the sentences: **b** words   29
Now you can read these words   30

Look at the pictures. Say the words.

apple

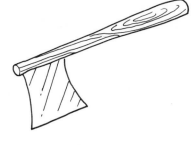

axe

Read these letters. Write them in your exercise book.

1. a   a   A   A
2. A   A   a   a
3. a   A   a   A

Draw these pictures. Say the words.

1.

apples

2.

ambulance

3.
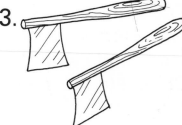

axes

Look at the pictures. Say the words.

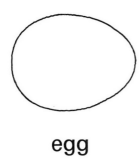

egg

elephant

Read these letters. Write them in your exercise book.

1.   **e**   **e**   **E**   **E**

2.   **E**   **E**   **e**   **e**

3.   **e**   **E**   **a**   **A**

Draw these pictures. Say the words.

1.   2.   3.

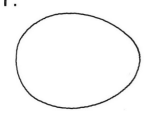

egg

apple

elephant

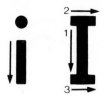

Look at the pictures. Say the words.

ink

Indian

Read these letters. Write them in your exercise book.

1.　i　　　i　　　I　　　I
2.　I　　　I　　　i　　　i
3.　i　　　I　　　e　　　E

Draw these pictures. Say the words.

1.

ink

2.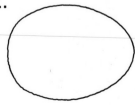

egg

3.

Indian

Look at the pictures. Say the words.

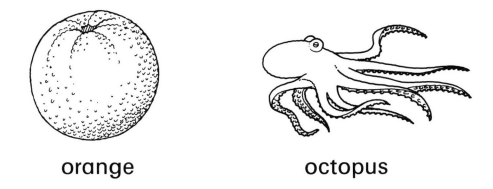

orange   octopus

Read these letters. Write them in your exercise book.

1.   o   o   O   O
2.   O   O   o   o
3.   o   O   i   I

Draw these pictures. Say the words.

1.   2.   3.

orange   Indian   octopus

5

Look at the pictures. Say the words.

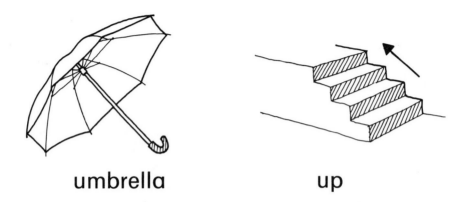

umbrella   up

Read these letters. Write them in your exercise book.

1.   u   u   U   U
2.   U   U   u   u
3.   u   U   o   O

Draw these pictures. Say the words.

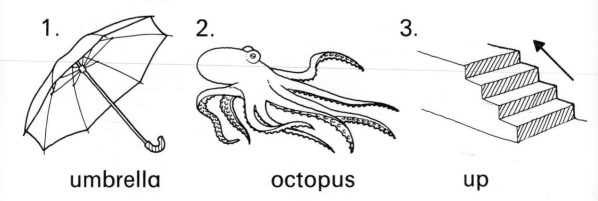

1.   2.   3.

umbrella   octopus   up

6

a e i o u

Look at each picture. Say the word.
Write the first letter of each word in your exercise book.

1.

2.
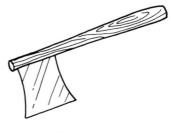

3.

4.

5.

6.
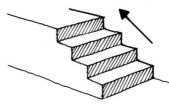

7.

8.

9.
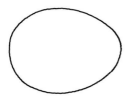

10.

Look at the pictures. Say the words.

man

match

mop

Read these letters. Write them in your exercise book.

1. m   m   M   M
2. M   M   m   m
3. m   M   u   U

Draw these pictures. Say the words.

1.

match

2.

orange

3.

mop

Read these words. Write them in your exercise book.

1. am   2. Mum

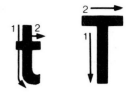

Look at the pictures. Say the words.

tap

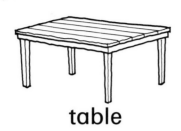
table

top

Read these letters. Write them in your exercise book.

1. t   t   T   T
2. T   T   t   t
3. t   T   m   M

Draw these pictures. Say the words.

1.
tap

2.
man

3.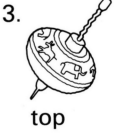
top

Read these words. Write them in your exercise book.

1. at   2. it   3. mat   4. met   5. Tim   6. Tom

Find the words in the bag with **m** in them.
Read these words. Write them in your exercise book.

1. _____   2. _____   3. _____

4. _____   5. _____   6. _____

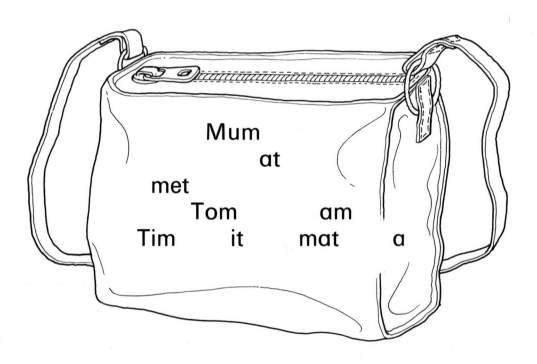

Mum
at
met
Tom   am
Tim   it   mat   a

Find the words in the bag with **t** in them.
Read these words. Write them in your exercise book.

1. _____   2. _____   3. _____

4. _____   5. _____   6. _____

Look at the pictures. Say the names.

Mum   Tom   Tim

Who is this? Write the answer in your exercise book.

1. _____

2. _____

3. _____

Read these sentences. Write them in your exercise book.

1. met . _____

2. met . _____

3. met . _____

4. met . _____

5. met . _____

Look at the pictures. Say the words.

sack   sun   sock

Read these letters. Write them in your exercise book.

1.   s   s   **S**   **S**
2.   **S**   **S**   s   s
3.   s   **S**   **t**   **T**

Read these words. Write them in your exercise book.

1. Sam   2. sat   3. set   4. sit

5. sum   6. mass   7. mess   8. miss

9. moss   10. toss

Find the words in the bag with **s** in them.
Read these words. Write them in your exercise book.

1. _____   2. _____   3. _____   4. _____   5. _____

6. _____   7. _____   8. _____   9. _____   10. _____

sit
Tim
Sam
Mum
sat
set
moss
mess
miss
mat
Tom
sum
toss
mass
met

Who sits? Look at the pictures. Say the names.

Sam   Tim   Mum   Tom

Read these sentences. Write them in your exercise book.

1. _____ sits.

2. _____ _____.

3. _____ _____.

4. _____ _____.

13

Look at the pictures. Say the words.

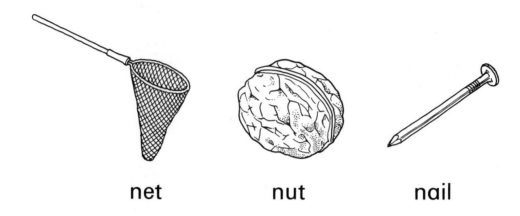

net   nut   nail

Read these letters. Write them in your exercise book.

1.   n   n   **N**   **N**
2.   **N**   **N**   n   n
3.   n   **N**   s   **S**

Read these words. Write them in your exercise book.

1. an   2. in   3. on   4. net   5. nit

6. not   7. nun   8. nut   9. Ann   10. inn

11. man   12. men   13. tan   14. ten   15. tin

16. sin   17. sun

Read these sentences. Write them in your exercise book.

1. It is a _____.

2. It is a _____.

3. It is a _____.

4. It is a _____.

5. It is a _____.

6. It is a _____.

7. It is a _____.

8. Ann's _____.

9. Tom's _____.

10. Ten nuts in a _____.

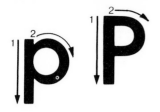

Look at the pictures. Say the words.

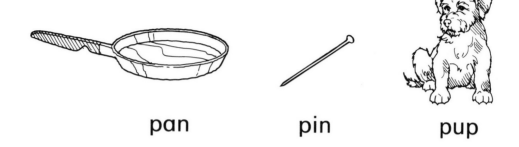

pan   pin   pup

Read these letters. Write them in your exercise book.

1.   p   p   **P**   **P**
2.   **P**   **P**   p   p
3.   p   **P**   n   **N**

Read these words. Write them in your exercise book.

1. Pam   2. pan   3. pat   4. pen   5. pet

6. pin   7. pit   8. pot   9. pup   10. map

11. mop   12. nap   13. nip   14. sap   15. sip

16. tap   17. tip   18. top

Read these sentences. Write them in your exercise book.

1. It is a _____.

2. It is a _____.

3. It is a _____.

4. It is Mum's _____.

5. It is Tom's _____.

6. It is Tim's _____.

7. It is Sam's _____.

8. A pup is in a _____.

9. Mum's _____.

10. Pam is _____.

Look at the pictures. Say the words.

cat   cap   cot

Read these letters. Write them in your exercise book.

1.   c   c   C   C
2.   C   C   c   c
3.   c   C   p   P

Read these words. Write them in your exercise book.

1. can   2. cap   3. cat

4. cot   5. cup   6. cut

Find the words in the bag with **c** in them.
Read these words. Write them in your exercise book.

1. _____   2. _____   3. _____

4. _____   5. _____   6. _____

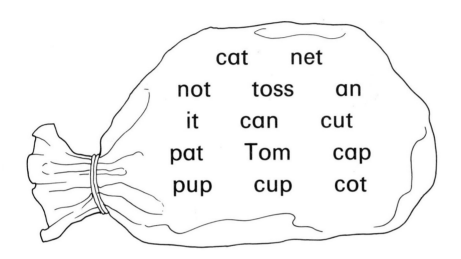

cat   net
not   toss   an
it   can   cut
pat   Tom   cap
pup   cup   cot

Read these sentences. Write them in your exercise book.

1. It is Sam's _____ .

2. It is Tom's _____ .

3. It is Mum's _____ .

4. It is Ann's _____ .

5. It is Tim's _____ .

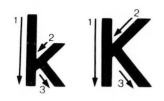

Look at the pictures. Say the words.

king   kitten   kettle

Read these letters. Write them in your exercise book.

1. k   k   K   K
2. K   K   k   k
3. k   K   c   C

Read these words. Write them in your exercise book.

1. Ken   2. kick   3. kit   4. kiss

5. cock   6. Mick   7. mock   8. neck

9. pack   10. peck   11. pick   12. sack

13. sick   14. sock   15. suck   16. tack

17. tick   18. tuck

Look at the pictures. Say the words.

Mum   Ken   Sam   Pam

Read these sentences. Write them in your exercise book.

1. It is  .

2. Is it Sam's ?

3. is sick.

4. picks up a .

5. picks up a .

6. kicks a BIRDS CUSTARD POWDER .

7. packs kit.

8. can kiss .

9. A sits on a .

10. picks up a .

21

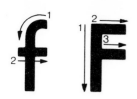

Look at the pictures. Say the words.

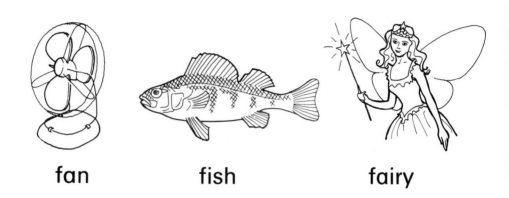

| fan | fish | fairy |

Read these letters. Write them in your exercise book.

1.	f	f	F	F
2.	F	F	f	f
3.	f	F	k	K

Read these words. Write them in your exercise book.

1. if   2. off   3. fan   4. fat

5. fen   6. fin   7. fit   8. fun

9. fuss   10. cuff   11. muff   12. puff

Find the words in the bag with **f** in them.
Read these words. Write them in your exercise book.

1. _____ 2. _____ 3. _____ 4. _____ 5. _____

6. _____ 7. _____ 8. _____ 9. _____ 10. _____

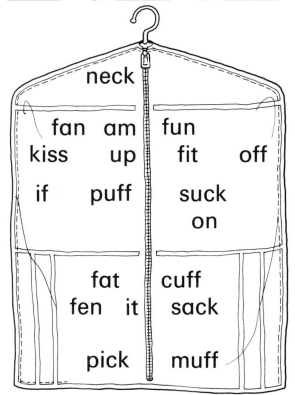

neck

fan am   fun
kiss   up   fit   off

if   puff   suck
                         on

fat   cuff
fen it   sack

pick   muff

Read the sentences. Choose the right words.
Write the sentences in your exercise book.

1. Mick is not (fat, fuss).

2. Mum is (fin, fit).

3. It is Pat's (fan, fin).

4. A pup is (fun, fan).

5. Sam kicks the tin (if, off) the mat.

Read these letters. Write them in your exercise book.

I   I   I   I   I

Read these sentences. Write them in your exercise book.

1. I am a .

2. I sat on a

3. I am a .

4. I can toss a

5. I kick a .

6. I met men.

7. I can pick up a .

8. I am not a

9. I met a  .

10. I can pick up a

24

the

Read these words. Write them in your exercise book.

the   the   the   the   the

Find the words in the bag that you can write with **the**.
Read these words. Write them in your exercise book.

1. the _____   2. the _____   3. the _____

4. the _____   5. the _____   6. the _____

7. the _____   8. the _____   9. the _____

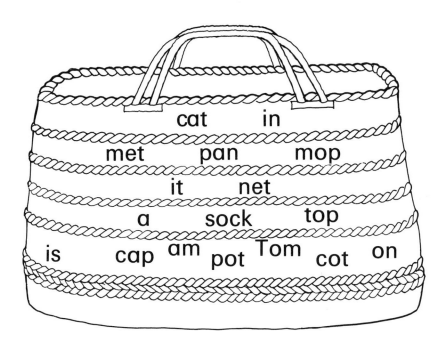

cat   in

met   pan   mop

it   net

a   sock   top

is   cap   am   pot   Tom   cot   on

Look at the pictures. Say the words.

log   lock   leg

Read these letters. Write them in your exercise book.

1.   I   I   L   L
2.   L   L   I   I
3.   I   L   f   F

Read these words. Write them in your exercise book.

1. lap   2. lass   3. less   4. let   5. lick

6. lip   7. lit   8. loss   9. lot   10. fell

11. fill   12. ill   13. kill   14. lock   15. luck

16. mill   17. nil   18. pal   19. pill   20. sell

21. sill   22. tell   23. till

Choose one of the words in each box to complete the sentence.
Write the sentence in your exercise book.

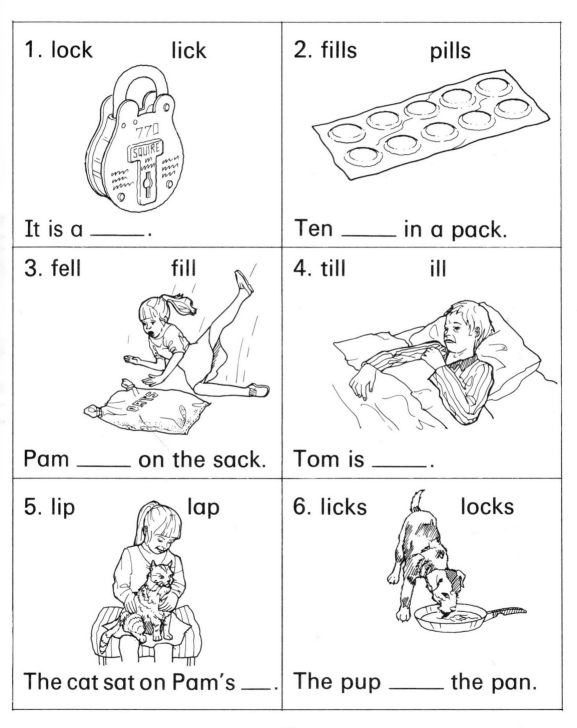

1. lock   lick

It is a _____.

2. fills   pills

Ten _____ in a pack.

3. fell   fill

Pam _____ on the sack.

4. till   ill

Tom is _____.

5. lip   lap

The cat sat on Pam's ___.

6. licks   locks

The pup _____ the pan.

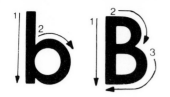

Look at the pictures. Say the words.

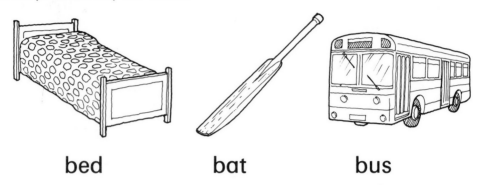

bed   bat   bus

Read these letters. Write them in your exercise book.

1.   b   b   **B**   **B**
2.   **B**   **B**   b   b
3.   b   **B**   I   L

Read these words. Write them in your exercise book.

1. back   2. ban   3. bat   4. bell   5. Ben

6. bet   7. bib   8. biff   9. Bill   10. bin

11. bit   12. Bob   13. boss   14. buck   15. bun

16. bus   17. but   18. cab   19. fib   20. mob

21. nib   22. pub   23. sob   24. tub

Choose one of the words in each box to complete the sentence.
Write the sentence in your exercise book.

1. bet   bat

Bob picks up a _____.

2. bus   bun

It is a _____.

3. bell   bit

It is Bill's _____.

4. Ben   bin

_____ fell on the mat.

5. but   buns

Ten _____.

6. tub   Bill

Tim sits on the _____.

Now you can read these words:

a	cab	ill	man	nit	pup	ten
am	can	in	map	not		the
an	cap	inn	mass	nun	sack	tick
Ann	cat	is	mat	nut	Sam	till
at	cock	it	men		sap	Tim
	cot		mess	off	sat	tin
back	cuff	Ken	met	on	sell	tip
ban	cup	kick	Mick		set	Tom
bat	cut	kill	mill	pack	sick	top
bell		kiss	miss	pal	sill	toss
Ben	fan	kit	mob	Pam	sin	tub
bet	fat		mock	pan	sip	tuck
bib	fell	lap	mop	pat	sit	
biff	fen	lass	moss	peck	sob	up
Bill	fib	less	muff	pen	sock	
bin	fill	let	Mum	pet	suck	
bit	fin	lick		pick	sum	
Bob	fit	lip	nap	pill	sun	
boss	fun	lit	neck	pin		
buck	fuss	lock	net	pit	tack	
bun		loss	nib	pot	tan	
bus	I	lot	nil	pub	tap	
but	if	luck	nip	puff	tell	

30